This book is dedicated to my son, Jason Jr.; you are my heart. To my husband, Jason Sr., thank you for allowing me to be myself and explore all my creative ideas. Finally, to my mom, who favors me. I thank God for each of you.

Manufactured in the United States of America
ISBN: 978-0-692-96685-3
Creative Design and Illustration by Courtney Monday
USA $14.95   Canada $16.95

Jason and the Cold Winter Day

written by: Jennifer Zimmerman, Ph.D., LPC

illustrated by: Courtney Monday

Jason loves school, and he loves the new responsibility that his parents gave him this school year.

This year, Jason is allowed to choose his own clothing, dress himself, and walk to school with friends that live on his street.

5

Every morning, Jason meets his friends, Joshua and Julia the twins and they all walk to school together.

On their walk to school they talk about all sorts of things like the twins dog, Bella. They also talk about all the fun they have in their robotics class and the big science project they have in STEM club.

While Jason was in his robotics group the school principal, Mrs. Bussey, came on the intercom and said, "Tomorrow, it will be very cold, so I want all students to dress in warm clothing, appropriate for the cold weather."

Jason is very busy trying to get his robot to walk so he did not listen to Mrs. Bussey, and he thinks wearing a coat is not cool. So he chose to ignore the announcement.

The next morning Jason got dressed. He put on his favorite khaki shorts, his blue polo shirt, and his brown moccasins, and headed for school. He forgot about the cold weather warning.

As Jason opened the door to his house he could feel the cold breeze. He noticed that ice was on the ground, and he considered getting his sweater, but school is right down the street so he left without it.

Joshua and Julia came to meet Jason dressed in their coats, hats, gloves, and scarves. They also have on pants and sweaters. Jason thought maybe I should get my coat, but he did not.

"Jason, where is your coat?" asked Julia. "Yeah Jason, where are your gloves?" asked Joshua. Jacob also walks to school that day, and he asked Jason, "Why are you wearing shorts, it is cold outside?" Jason now felt embarrassed. Even Bella, the twin's dog, was wearing her sparkling monogrammed sweater.

As Jason arrived at school his teacher, the school counselor, and the principal questioned his clothing. The counselor, Mr. Del Rosario, calls Jason's parents. Jason's mother left work to bring him some warm clothes to wear at school.

"Jason, I am very disappointed that you came to school dressed inappropriately for the weather," said Jason's mother. "I no longer trust you to choose your own clothing and dress yourself."

"From now on daddy or I will choose your clothing for you, and help you dress in the mornings."

Jason apologized to his mother and learned a lesson about dressing for the weather. Now, he knows when it's cold outside he must dress warmly. Even his mother dressed warmly and she is an adult.

Jason did regain his parent's trust. He is allowed to choose his own clothes again and dresses himself for school. Thanks to his parents, friends, and teachers he never leaves the house without the proper clothing.

Help Jason Dress for the Weather

Winter	Spring

Summer	Fall

Match the clothing with the season.

Pants
Gloves
Shorts
Scarf
Skirt
Hat
Dress
Boots
Sandals
Gym shoes
Socks
Tights
Sweater
Short sleeved shirt
Long sleeved shirt
Tank top
Coat

Jennifer Zimmerman, Ph.D., LPC, has worked in education for over 15 years, and loves incorporating children's literature when counseling children. Jennifer lives in Atlanta with her husband and son.

Made in the USA
Monee, IL
02 May 2022

95767743R00021